Let's dress Jane...

The Revolt of Mamie Stover 1956

Gentlemen Prefer Blondes, 1953

Underwater! 1955

The French Line
1954

Son of Paleface
1952

Macao
1952

His Kind of
Woman
1951

Nightclub act
Madrid, 1960

Macao
1952

The Paleface
1948

The Fuzzy Pink
Nightgown
1957

The Fuzzy Pink
Nightgown
1957

Gentlemen Prefer
Blondes
1953

Gentlemen Prefer
Blondes
1953

Gentlemen Prefer
Blondes
1953

The Paleface
1948

The Outlaw
1943

The Paleface
1948

Hot Blood
1956

Foxfire
1955

Gentlemen Marry
Brunettes
1955

1

2

*Gentlemen Prefer
Blondes
1953*

2

3

*The Revolt
of Mamie Stover
1956*

3

*Gentlemen Prefer
Blondes
1953*